Baby Kangaroo

AT HOME IN THE OUTBACK

ILLUSTRATED BY LINDA HOLT AYRISS
WRITTEN BY JENNIFER BOUDART

ISBN-13: 978-0-7853-1217-8
ISBN-10: 0-7853-1217-X

8 7 6 5 4 3 2 1

The red gum tree shades the Australian outback on warm afternoons.

Kangaroos know this well, so they rest under the trees during the hot summer days. They lie on their sides, with their long legs stretched behind them.

One kangaroo does not want to take a nap. His name is Joey, and he wants to play.

A kangaroo is called a joey when it is a baby. Joey is only a few months old. Like all kangaroos, he has strong back legs, large feet, and a long tail. When Joey moves, it's easy to see why his legs and body look this way.

He hops! Joey bounces along on his back legs, using his tail for balance.

Joey finds two other young kangaroos who are awake, too. They start to wrestle each other, poking tummies and tugging on ears and tails. Little Joey leads the others in a hopping race.

A clucking noise makes him stop suddenly. It is his mother calling him. She uses the sound to tell Joey that he has wandered too far from her.

Joey returns to his mother. He is very tired now. He climbs headfirst into a small pouch in his mother's tummy! The pouch is the perfect size for her baby. Only Joey's legs are sticking out. Then he turns himself around in the pouch so he can see.

A kangaroo mother's pouch makes a great built-in bed for her babies.

A kangaroo stamps its foot on the ground. That sound means danger! Joey's mother lifts her head and sniffs the air. Suddenly, a dingo dog comes running from the trees.

The kangaroos must escape! They jump away, flying through the air. Joey ducks down into his mother's pouch. His mother has never moved so fast!

The kangaroos jump fast and far. The pack of dingo dogs can't keep up. Soon the dingoes drop back. The kangaroos are safe, but they keep on moving. They're heading toward a patch of rain clouds.

The kangaroos know that tasty green grass grows wherever rain has fallen. The group reaches its new home before dark.

Joey hops to a pool filled with rainwater. The pool is new to him. The land where he lives is normally very dry. Joey looks into the water. He sees another kangaroo looking back at him! Who is it?

Joey leans closer to look in the water at the stranger's face. Oops! Joey dips his nose in the water and gets all wet.

The water feels very good. Joey hops right into the puddle. Soon other young kangaroos join him there. They discover what older kangaroos already know: water is fun!